Printed and Published in Great Britain
by D. C. THOMSON & Co., Ltd., 185 Fleet Street,
London EC4A 2HS.
© D. C. THOMSON & Co., 1991.
ISBN 0-85116-521-4

8

10

14

15

B

20

22

23

Follow Dan and Buster on the run — Page 46

DAN'S WAY-OUT WEST

31

33

37

39

40

41

At lunchtime—

REMEMBER TO FIX THAT FRONT DOOR YOU BUST, DAN — OR YOU WON'T GET THE OTHER SIX COW-PIES!

Watch the hand at the window—

AW, AUNT AGGIE, AH'M A GROWIN' BOY!

SLEEPING DRAUGHT

MMM! AH FEEL A MITE TUCKERED — TIME FOR A BIT OF SHUT EYE.

So—

SNORE!

43

47

48

Continued on Page 68.

So—

Howdy, folks.

It's the Cactusville Cattle Market and the local ranch owners are in town to buy up cattle. The biggest buy is a herd of buffalo which has been split amongst four neighbouring farmers. You have each been hired by one of the farmers to get his share of the herd home first.
So let's get them steers a'rollin'!

RULES:—
This is a game for two to four players. You will need a dice and coloured counters (coloured pieces of card will do just as well). Each player must start on their own coloured circle in the middle, the highest roll of the dice deciding who goes first. The players must follow their coloured arrow and go round the board in an anti-clockwise direction. If they land on a square with instructions on it they must follow these instructions. The winner is the first to get his or her coloured counter to the ranch of the same colour.
(A longer version of the game can be played where each player has an equal amount of counters. When each throws they can then decide which counter to move. The winner here shall be the one to get all their counters home!)

RUN OUT OF WATER. GO BACK TO THE RIVER FOR MORE.

STOP TO LET EXPRESS PASS. MISS A TURN.

BUILD A BRIDGE OVER RIVER. MISS A TURN.

YOU ARE NOW ENTERING BANDIT COUNTRY.

FLOODING DRIVES YOU BACK TWO.

FRIENDLY INDIANS ESCORT YOU THROUGH TERRITORY. MOVE ON THREE.

CUT YOUR WAY THROUGH CACTUS VALLEY. MISS A TURN.

57

80

MAINSTREET

BARBER'S

DAN'S JUST BEEN IN FOR A SHAVE AND A HAIRCUT!

HAIR GEL

BOOTS 'N' SHOES

CLANG!

JUST REPAIRIN' DAN'S SUNDAY BEST!

HORSE SHOES

BUTCHER

SORRY, FOLKS!

SOLD OUT!
AUNT AGGIE'S MAKIN' DAN'S WEEKLY SUPPLY OF COW-PIES!

SHERIFF'S OFFICE

WHEN I TOLD DAN TO RUN IN BLACK JAKE — I MEANT THROUGH THE DOOR!

CACTUSVILLE

SILVER DOLLAR SALOON

POOR GUY DRANK SOME OF DAN'S OWL HOOT JUICE!

OWL HOOT JUICE

YEEHAR!

SOUVENIRS

WELL, HE IS CACTUSVILLE'S MOST FAMOUS SON!

CACTUSVILLE ODEON

○ ○ NOW SHOWING ○ ○

○ A FISTFUL OF COW·PIES ○

IT'S MAH FAVOURITE FILM!

QUEUE HERE